Happiness is ...

The best of the Hamlet moments

CHANCELLOR
PRESS

First published in Great Britain 1993

Bloomsbury Publishing Limited, 2 Soho Square, London W1V 5DE

Compilation copyright © 1993 by Gallaher Limited

Introduction copyright © 1993 by William Rushton

This 1994 edition published by Chancellor Press, Michelin House, 81 Fulham Road, London SW3 6RB

Cartoon Credits

Caldwell: Hamlet moments 1, 42, 55, 94, 95, 102.

'Danny': Hamlet moment 88.

de la **Nougerede**: Hamlet moments 16, 84. **Pat Drennan**: Hamlet moments 28, 65, 66, 67, 79. **Emms**: Hamlet moment 45.

Fiddy: Hamlet moments 5, 26, 58, 65. **Noel Ford**: Hamlet moments 19, 93, 96. **Haldane**: Hamlet moments 15, 20, 60, 82, 83, 91.

Julie Hollings: Hamlet moment 75. **'Holte'**: Hamlet moments 76, 99. **'Larry'**: Hamlet moments 10, 24, 51, 92.

McLachlan: Hamlet moments 2, 13, 23, 48, 70, 71, 74. **David Myers**: Hamlet moments 9, 30, 31, 56, 66.

'Sax': Hamlet moments 35, 38, 40, 41, 77, 80, 87. **Mike Williams**: Hamlet moments 72, 106.

All other cartoons courtesy of CDP.

A CIP catalogue record for this book is available from the British Library

ISBN 1 85152 6331

Front cover cartoon by Pat Drennan

Designed by Fielding Rowinski

Printed by Cronion S.A., Barcelona, Spain

Introduction

It is said that every comedian wants to play Hamlet. I have always had serious doubts about this. It's far too much to remember, for one, and contains very few laughs. (Actually not having to get laughs is quite relaxing, so there may be an element of truth there.) I shall start again. It would be fair to say that very few comedians would not have given their comedy teeth to have appeared in a Hamlet commercial. I was reminded how good they were when putting them all (or most of them) together in a video to mourn their passing on TV. It's hard to believe that the first one appeared on telly in 1964. In black and white. And in many parts of the country, silent. Like so much of my early career.

The best thing about Hamlet commercials is that we know the feeling. Bored. Frustrated. At risk, perhaps. In pain. Then that chord from Jacques Loussier. . . and sod it, so what? Puff, puff. All human life is there.

It was a sad day – it usually is – when Nanny struck and the commercials were no more. But this book is evidence of the resilience of the human spirit. Up they popped as cartoons on hoardings and in newspapers. There are some unforgettable ones in here too. That Hamlet moment is well known to all of us.

One thing I don't understand, Inspector, in none of the commercials and nowhere in this book has the eponymous Hamlet appeared. I can see the gloomy Dane on an Elsinore battlement ... "To be, or not to be ... Oh sod it!" Ping! and lighting up.

Thank you, Hamlet,

William Rushton.

HAMLET MOMENT

....

I

HAMLET MOMENT

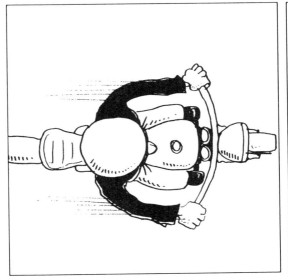 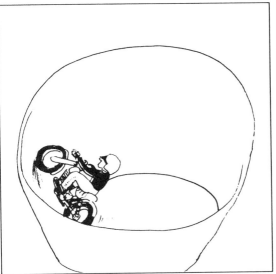 

HAMLET MOMENT

HAMLET MOMENT

4

HAMLET MOMENT

5

HAMLET MOMENT

Happiness
is a
cigar called
Hamlet.

HAMLET MOMENT

HAMLET MOMENT

From an idea by George Bayliss

HAMLET MOMENT
....
10

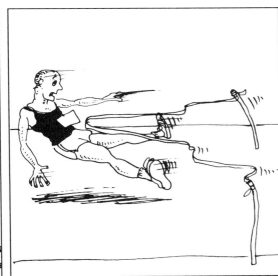

HAMLET MOMENT

HAMLET MOMENT

12

HAMLET MOMENT

 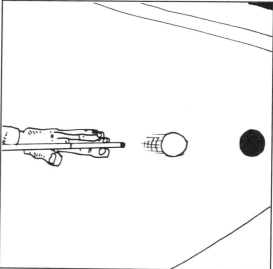 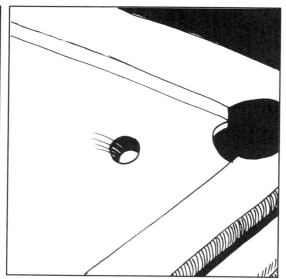

HAMLET MOMENT
....
14

HAMLET MOMENT

From an idea by Dale Robinson

HAMLET MOMENT

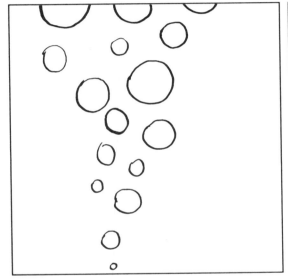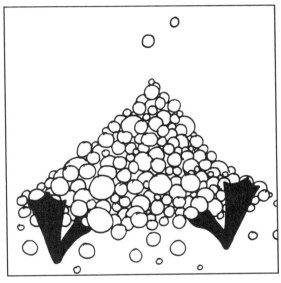

HAMLET MOMENT

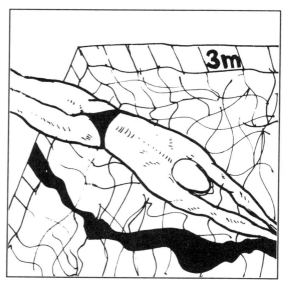  

HAMLET MOMENT

HAMLET MOMENT

HAMLET MOMENT

HAMLET MOMENT

HAMLET MOMENT

HAMLET MOMENT

HAMLET MOMENT

HAMLET MOMENT

HAMLET MOMENT

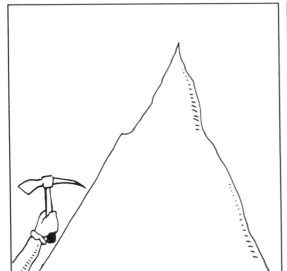  

HAMLET MOMENT

From an idea by Tony Doe

HAMLET MOMENT

HAMLET MOMENT

HAMLET MOMENT

HAMLET MOMENT

HAMLET MOMENT

HAMLET MOMENT

  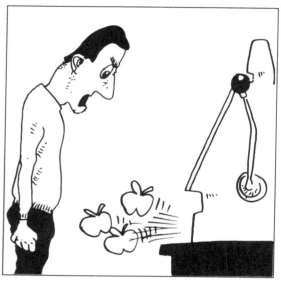

HAMLET MOMENT

From an idea by Claire Brown

HAMLET MOMENT

HAMLET MOMENT

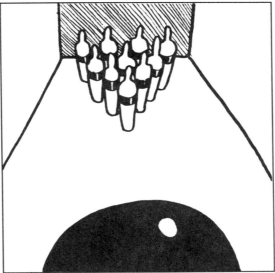

HAMLET MOMENT

HAMLET MOMENT

From an idea by S. Nelson

HAMLET MOMENT

HAMLET MOMENT

HAMLET MOMENT

HAMLET MOMENT

HAMLET MOMENT

HAMLET MOMENT

HAMLET MOMENT

HAMLET MOMENT

HAMLET MOMENT
. . . .

HAMLET MOMENT

HAMLET MOMENT

HAMLET MOMENT

HAMLET MOMENT

HAMLET MOMENT

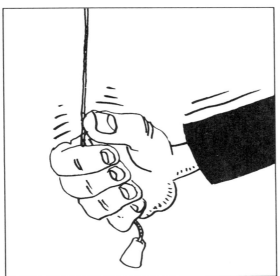

HAMLET MOMENT

HAMLET MOMENT

HAMLET MOMENT

From an idea by W.A. Edwards

HAMLET MOMENT

....

5 6

HAMLET MOMENT

HAMLET MOMENT

58

HAMLET MOMENT

HAMLET MOMENT

HAMLET MOMENT

From an idea by L.G. Largent

HAMLET MOMENT

HAMLET MOMENT

From an idea by A.C. Hawkins

HAMLET MOMENT

HAMLET MOMENT

HAMLET MOMENT

  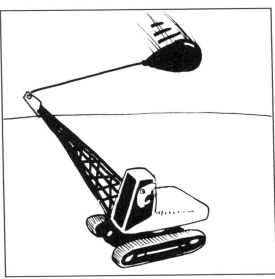

HAMLET MOMENT

HAMLET MOMENT

Happiness is a cigar called Hamlet.

HAMLET MOMENT

HAMLET MOMENT

HAMLET MOMENT

HAMLET MOMENT

HAMLET MOMENT

HAMLET MOMENT

From an idea by R. Wood

HAMLET MOMENT

HAMLET MOMENT

HAMLET MOMENT

77

HAMLET MOMENT

HAMLET MOMENT

From an idea by Timothy Thouless

HAMLET MOMENT

....

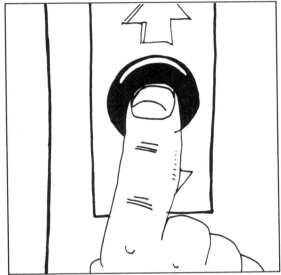  

HAMLET MOMENT

HAMLET MOMENT

HAMLET MOMENT

From an idea by Ann Workman

HAMLET MOMENT

84

HAMLET MOMENT

8 5

HAMLET MOMENT

HAMLET MOMENT

HAMLET MOMENT

HAMLET MOMENT

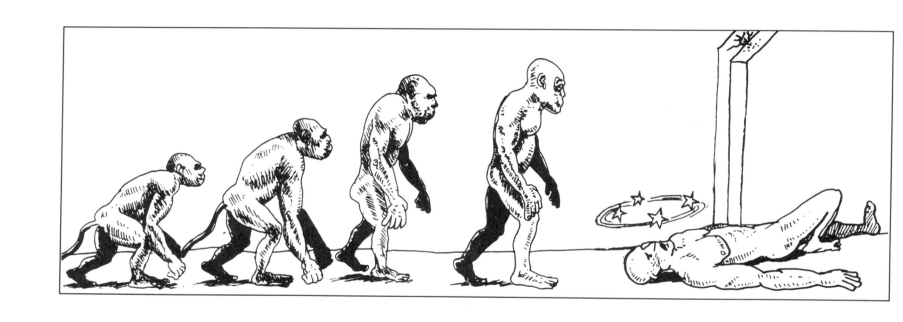

HAMLET MOMENT

HAMLET MOMENT

HAMLET MOMENT

HAMLET MOMENT

HAMLET MOMENT

From an idea by G. Monaghan

HAMLET MOMENT

From an idea by Ivan

HAMLET MOMENT
....

HAMLET MOMENT

 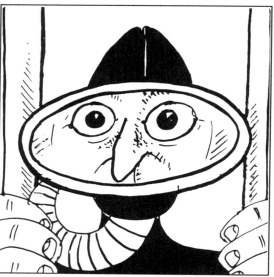 

HAMLET MOMENT

HAMLET MOMENT

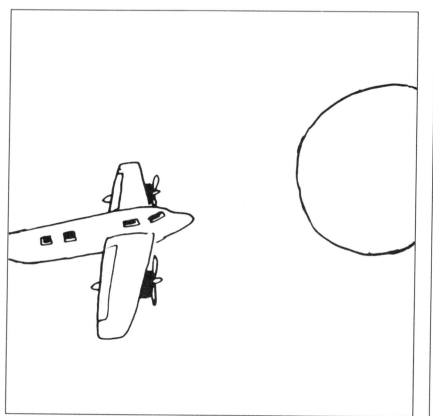 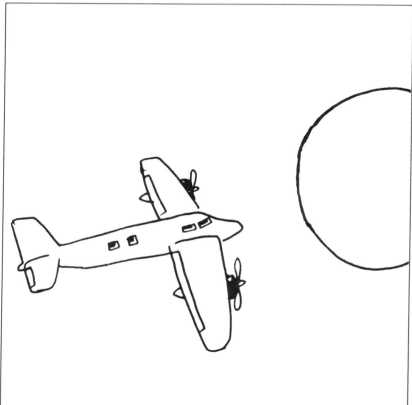

HAMLET MOMENT

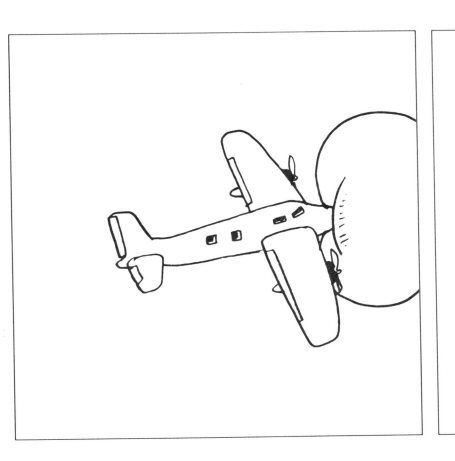

Happiness is a cigar called Hamlet.

HAMLET MOMENT

HAMLET MOMENT

HAMLET MOMENT

HAMLET MOMENT

HAMLET MOMENT

HAMLET MOMENT

HAMLET MOMENT